How to use this book

Follow the advice, in italics, given for you on each page.
Support the children as they read the text that is shaded in cream.
***Praise** the children at every step!*

Detailed guidance is provided in the Read Write Inc. *Handbook*

9 reading activities

Children:

1. practise reading the speed sounds

2. read the green, red and challenge words for the story

3. listen as you read the introduction

4. discuss the vocabulary check with you

5. read the story

6. re-read the story and discuss the 'questions to talk about'

7. read the story with fluency and expression

8. answer the questions to 'read and answer'

9. practise reading the speed words

Read
Write Inc.

An inclusive literacy programme by Ruth Miskin

3

Speed sounds

Consonants   *Say the pure sounds (do not add 'uh')*

f	l	m	n	r	s	v	z	sh	th	ng
ff	ll	mm	nn	rr	ss	ve	zz			nk
			kn				s			

b	c	d	g	h	j	p	qu	t	w	x	y	ch
bb	k	dd	gg			pp		tt	wh			tch
	ck											

Vowels   *Say the sounds in and out of order*

at	hen	in	on	up	day	see	high	blow
	head					happy	find	no

zoo	look	car	for	fair	whirl	shout	boy
			door				spoil
			snore				

*Each box contains one sound but sometimes more than one grapheme. Focus graphemes are **circled**.*

Green words

Read in Fred Talk (pure sounds)

flung   sheet   look   shook   cook   stood   seen   thing   pink
bright   light   night   right   knight   tight   might   find   kind

Read in syllables

a`way → away          al`ways → always
mid`night → midnight  moon`light → moonlight
night`light → nightlight  day`light → daylight

Read the root word first and then with the ending

rush → rushed   pack → packing
fright → frighten → frightened   light → lighting

Red words

there   watch   small   what   some   be   me   of
was   my   the   to   now   she   you

Challenge words

under   supper   eyes

Danny and the Bump-a-lump

Introduction

Are you scared of the dark?
Do you ever imagine there are things in your bedroom that
aren't really there? Danny is frightened. He's sure there is
something under his bed. Mum keeps sending him back to
bed but Danny really believes there's a Bump-a-lump there.

What will Mum do?

Story written by Gill Munton
Illustrated by Tim Archbold

Vocabulary check

Discuss the meaning (as used in the story) after the children have read each word.

	definition:	sentence:
moonlight	the light from a full moon	Bright moonlight
flung	threw off	I flung back the sheet.
supper	evening meal	She was lighting the gas to cook her supper.
knight	a soldier in metal armour	It was a knight to fight the Bump-a-lump.
nightlight	a lamp	In the knight's head there was a nightlight.
slid between the sheets	cuddled down into bed	I slid between the sheets and shut my eyes tight.

Punctuation to note in this story:
1. Capital letters to start sentences and full stop to end sentences
2. Capital letters for names
3. Exclamation marks to show anger, shock and surprise
4. 'Wait and see' dots......

Danny and the Bump-a-lump

Midnight. Bright moonlight.

There was a thing under my bed ...

Aaaaaaagh! Help!

I flung back the sheet and went to find Mum.

She was sitting on the settee, watching "The Highjack" on TV.

Mum: Danny! Back to bed, right away!

Me: But I've got a thing under my bed.

Mum: What is it?

Me: It's a Bump-a-lump.

Mum: What's a Bump-a-lump?

Me: Just a Bump-a-lump.

Mum: Is it there in the daylight, or just in the night?

Me: Just in the night.

Mum: Is it big or small?

I shook my head.

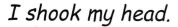

Mum: Is it red, or green, or pink, or ...

I shook my head.

Mum: Tell me, Danny. Have you seen this Bump-a-lump?

Me: No. But it's there, all right.

And I'm frightened of it!

Tell it to go away!

Mum: Don't be silly.

Go back to bed.

The next night ...

Bright moonlight.

And there was still a thing under my bed!

Aaaaagh! Help!

I flung back the sheet and
rushed off to find Mum.

She was lighting the gas to cook supper.

Mum: Danny! Back to bed, right away!

Me: But, Mum, I've got a thing under my bed!

It's a Bump-a-lump!

It's always there, in the night!

It might be big, and it might be small!

It might be red, or green, or pink

or maybe gold with black spots!

And I'm frightened of it!

Tell it to go away!

Mum: What you need is something to frighten the Bump-a-lump.

The next night...

Mum stood something next to my bed.

It was a knight. The right kind of knight

for a fight with a Bump-a-lump.

In the knight's head, there was a nightlight.

I slid between the sheets and shut my eyes tight.

Mum: Right! This will send the Bump-a-lump away!

You will be all right tonight.

Me: Thanks, Mum.

Mum: Do you think you can get to sleep?

Me: I might ... I think I might ...

Mum: I'm having a look under the bed ...

That's not a Bump-a-lump!

It's just a bit of fluff!

Goodnight, sleep tight, kiss kiss!

Me: Zzzzz! Zzzzz!

Questions to talk about

Re-read the page. Read the question to the children. Tell them whether it is a **FIND IT** question or **PROVE IT** question.

FIND IT

✔ Turn to the page

✔ Read the question

✔ Find the answer

PROVE IT

✔ Turn to the page

✔ Read the question

✔ Find your evidence

✔ Explain why

Page 9:	PROVE IT	*Why did Danny get up?*
Page 10:	PROVE IT	*Why did Mum ask Danny if the Bump-a-lump was big or small?*
Page 11:	PROVE IT	*Do you think Mum believes Danny about the Bump-a-lump?*
Page 12:	FIND IT	*What was Mum doing when Danny got up?*
Page 13:	PROVE IT	*Why doesn't Danny know what the Bump-a-lump looks like?*
Page 14:	PROVE IT	*Why does mum get the knight?*
Page 15:	PROVE IT	*What was really under the bed?* *Do you think this is what Danny was really scared of?*

Questions to read and answer

(Children complete without your help.)

1. Mum was sitting on **the floor / the settee /** the bed.

2. Danny thinks about the Bump-a-lump **at night / in the daylight.**

3. Mum was cooking **her supper / looking at her book / having a nap.**

4. Mum put **a Bump-a-lump / a teddy / a knight** next to Danny's bed.

5. There was **a bit of fluff / a Bump-a-lump / a bad dog** under the bed.

Speed words

flung	sheet	settee	something	fight
rushed	tight	right	tonight	daylight
lighting	frightened	there	small	what
watch	find	kind	green	her